SRA Open Court Reading

Book 1

Games

•

Folktales

SRA Open Court Reading

Book 1

Program Authors

Marilyn Jager Adams
Carl Bereiter
Anne McKeough
Robbie Case
Marsha Roit
Jan Hirshberg
Michael Pressley
Iva Carruthers
Gerald H. Treadway, Jr.

A Division of The McGraw·Hill Companies

Columbus, Ohio

Acknowledgments

Grateful acknowledgment is given to the following publishers and copyright owners for permissions granted to reprint selections from their publications. All possible care has been taken to trace ownership and secure permission for each selection included.

Carolrhoda Books Inc.: JAFTA by Hugh Lewin, illustrations by Lisa Kopper. Text copyright © 1981 by Hugh Lewin. Illustrations copyright © 1981 by Lisa Kopper. Reprinted with permission of Carolrhoda Books, Inc., Minneapolis, MN. All rights reserved.

Crown Publishers Inc.: **THE CHASE: A KUTENAI INDIAN TALE by Beatrice Tanaka, illustrated by Michel Gay. Translation copyright © 1991 by Crown Publishers, Inc. Copyright © 1990 by Kaleidoscope, Paris.** Reprinted by arrangement with Crown Publishers, Inc.

Dutton Children's Books, a division of Penguin Putnam Inc.: MATTHEW AND TILLY by Rebecca C. Jones, illustrated by Beth Peck. Copyright © 1991 by Rebecca C. Jones, text, illustrations Copyright © 1991 by Beth Peck. Used by permission of Dutton Children's Books, a division of Penguin Putnam Inc.

Edizioni E. Elle: "Little Green Riding Hood" from TELEPHONE TALES, by Gianni Rodari. Copyright © Edizioni E. Elle, Trieste, Italy. Reprinted with permission of Edizioni E. Elle.

HarperCollins Publishers: "The Big Team Relay Race" from ON YOUR MARK, GET SET, GO! by LEONARD KESSLER. Copyright © 1972 by Leonard Kessler. Used by permission of HarperCollins Publishers. "A Game Called Piggle" from PIGGLE by CROSBY BONSALL. Copyright © 1973 by Crosby Bonsall. Used by permission of HarperCollins Publishers.

Holiday House, Inc.: ANANSI AND THE TALKING MELON by Eric A. Kimmel, illustrated by Janet Stevens. Text copyright © 1994 by Eric A. Kimmel. Illustrations copyright © 1994 by Janet Stevens. All rights reserved. Reprinted by permission of Holiday House, Inc.

Scholastic Inc.: From THE BOSSY GALLITO retold by Lucía M. González, illustrated by Lulu Delacre. Text copyright © 1994 by Lucía M. González. Illustration copyright © 1994 by Lulu Delacre. Reprinted by permission of Scholastic Inc.

Photo Credits
32, © Mark Lawrence; **118(b),** ©Cynthia Del Conte; **144(b),** ©Ted Haberman.

Unit Opener Illustrations
10–11 Hilary Knight; **82–83** Henrik Drescher.

SRA/McGraw-Hill

A Division of The McGraw·Hill Companies

Send all inquiries to:
SRA/McGraw-Hill
8787 Orion Place
Columbus, Ohio 43240-4027

Printed in the United States of America.

ISBN 0-02-830949-9

4 5 6 7 8 9 RRD 04 03 02 01 00

Program Authors

Marilyn Jager Adams, Ph.D.
BBN Technologies

Carl Bereiter, Ph.D.
University of Toronto

Anne McKeough, Ph.D.
University of Toronto

Robbie Case, Ph.D.
University of Toronto

Marsha Roit, Ph.D.
National Reading Consultant

Jan Hirshberg, Ed.D.

Michael Pressley, Ph.D.
University of Notre Dame

Iva Carruthers, Ph.D.
Northeastern Illinois University

Gerald H. Treadway, Jr., Ed.D.
San Diego State University

Table *of* Contents

Table *of* Contents

We all like to play games. But can we learn from games, too? Maybe we can. See what Homer and Bear, Jafta, the animals, and Matthew and Tilly find out about themselves while playing games.

11

A Game Called Piggle

from PIGGLE

by Crosby Bonsall

"Oh, Bear," Homer said, "will you play a game with me?"
Bear said, "Yes, I will. What shall we play?"

"Do you know a game called
Piggle?" Homer asked.
"Piggle . . . Piggle," Bear said.
"Piggle like triggle, hmmmm."

"Triggle, Bear?" Homer said.
"Triggle," Bear said.
"Triggle like biggle."
"Oh," said Homer.

"Let me think," said Bear.
"Piggle like miggle."
"Miggle, Bear?" Homer said.
"Miggle like diggle," Bear said.
"Oh," said Homer.

"Give me time," said Bear.
"Let me see now, we have triggle and
biggle, miggle and diggle like Piggle."

"Oh, *I* see," cried Homer. "Let me try.
Wiggle, giggle, sniggle and figgle
like Piggle. That's *it*, Bear. I can play!"

"Yes, you can," cried Bear.
"Maybe I know the game of Piggle
after all. It sounds nice."
"Yes, it does," Homer said.
"Let's piggle some more.
Ishy, wishy, fishy, dishy."

Bear sang, "Diddley, widdley,
fiddley, riddley."
And together they sang,
"Mumpity, wumpity,
dumpity, lumpity."

19

A Game Called Piggle

Meet the Author and Illustrator

Crosby Bonsall was born in Queens, New York. She was always interested in art and went to school to study it. After graduating, she worked for advertising firms. She later wrote and drew illustrations for over 40 children's books. Sometimes she wrote and illustrated her stories using the last name Newell, her last name before she got married.

Theme Connections

Think About It

Piggle is a word game that uses rhymes and nonsense words.

- What word games have you played?
- Do you like playing them alone or with someone?

Look at the Concept/Question Board. Are there any questions on it that you can answer now? Do you have any new questions about games? Write the questions on the Board. Maybe the next reading will help answer your question.

Record Ideas

 Write the anwers to these questions in your Writing Journal:

- Do you like playing word games?
- Why?

Make a Piggle Dictionary

In small groups, select a nonsense word from the selection, and copy that word on a sheet of paper. Then find words that rhyme and write them on the paper also.

Jafta

A Shared Reading Story

Hugh Lewin

illustrated by Lisa Kopper

When I'm happy, said Jafta, I purr like
a lioncub,

or skip like a spider,

or laugh like a hyena.

And sometimes I want to jump like an impala,

and dance like a zebra,

or just nuzzle like a rabbit.

When I get tired, I like lazing in the
sun like a lizard,
or wallowing warm like a hippo,
and feeling cuddly like a lamb.

But when I get cross, I stamp like an elephant and grumble like a warthog.

(I don't often get cross, said Jafta.)

And I can be as strong as a rhino.

Sometimes I want to be as tall as a giraffe, as long as a snake.

And I want to run as fast as a cheetah, as quick as an ostrich,

or swing through the trees like a monkey, and fly high high high like an eagle,

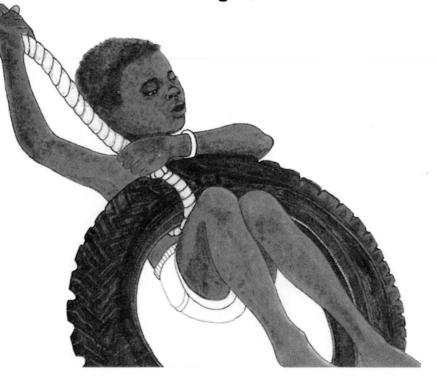

or just stand very still, like a crane on one leg.

But actually, said Jafta,
I don't think there's anything quite so
nice as being a flamingo flying off into
the sunset . . .

Jafta

Meet the Author

Hugh Lewin was born in Lydenburg, South Africa; however, his family was from England. Hugh moved to England as an adult. He later wrote the Jafta stories to teach his daughters about where he grew up in South Africa.

Meet the Illustrator

Lisa Kopper grew up in Chicago, Illinois. When she was in her twenties, she moved to England where she became an illustrator. Since then she has illustrated more than 100 children's books, many of which have been published throughout the world. She is well-known for her multicultural work, of which the Jafta Family Series is the most famous.

Theme Connections

Talk About It

Think about these questions, then talk about them with a group of your classmates.

- Do you think that Jafta was really with the animals?
- Do you think Jafta was just imagining the animals to have fun?
- When do you use your imagination to have fun?

If you have any questions about games, post them on the Concept/Question Board.

Record Ideas

When do you use your imagination?

- In your Writing Journal, write about a time when you used your imagination to have fun.

Plan for the Unit Activity

- Do you want to have any imagining in your new game?
- Meet with your group and talk about it.

The Big Team Relay Race

from ON YOUR MARK, GET SET, GO!
by Leonard Kessler
illustrated by Charmie Curran

The animals are playing games. The teams are the Yankees, the Tigers, and the Pirates. Worm wants to play, but she is not on a team.

"All teams line up for the big team relay race," Owl said.

Dog, Frog, and Turtle went to the starting line. Duck, Rabbit, and Cat waited down the track. Frog and Turtle each had a little stick.

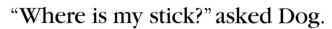

"Where is my stick?" asked Dog.

"Who has the stick?" asked Owl.

"Get a stick. I need a stick!" yelled Dog.

Worm wiggled over to Owl.

"I am ready, Coach," said Worm.

"Hey, Worm," said Owl. "You can be Dog's stick!"

"Wow! I am on a team!" said Worm. "I'm a Yankee!"

"Okay," said Owl. "Each of you must
run with your stick. Then pass it on to your
other team member. And remember,"
said Owl, "the stick must cross the finish line."

"Okay," said little Bird.
"ON YOUR MARK, GET SET, GO!"

Zoom! Down the track they ran.
Cat, Rabbit, and Duck were waiting.
"Here they come," yelled Duck.

Turtle gave his stick to Cat.
Frog gave his stick to Rabbit.
And Dog gave his stick to Duck.
    Zoom! Cat, Rabbit, and Duck ran down
the track.

"Duck is winning, Duck is winning!" yelled Dog.
Duck smiled and waved to the cheering crowd.

She tripped over her big web feet and fell into a big mud puddle. Squoosh!

"Get up, Duck," shouted Dog.

"Yikes," yelled Duck, "I am stuck in the mud!"

"Don't worry, Duck," said Worm. "I will win the race for our team."

Worm wiggled and wiggled.
She wiggled past the finish line—first!
"WORM IS THE WINNER!" yelled Spider.
"The Yankees win!" shouted Dog.

"Let's give a cheer for Worm," yelled Owl.
"Squiggle squiggle,
Who can wiggle?
Wiggle wiggle
Wiggle Worm.
Yay, yay, Worm!"

The Big Team Relay Race

Meet the Author

Leonard Kessler was born in Ohio in 1921. He was an artist and designer when he met his wife, who was an author. Together with his wife, Kessler has written and illustrated dozens of children's books. Many of their ideas for books came from their own children. Whenever he can, Kessler enjoys painting with watercolors as a hobby.

Meet the Illustrator

Charmie Curran has always liked to draw. She now lives in Bow, New Hampshire, with her husband Michael, their two children, Allyx and Max, two dogs, two zebra finches, a cat, and eleven assorted chickens.

Theme Connections

Think About It

- Owl made up a cheer for Worm. What other story does the cheer remind you of?

Talk About It

Most games are the same in some ways and different in other ways. How are a relay race and the two other games we read about the same and different? Here are some questions to talk about:

- How is a relay race the same as the game Piggle? How is it different?
- How is a relay race the same as Jafta's pretend game? How is it different?

Look at the Concept/Question Board. Are there any questions on it that you can answer now? Do you have any new questions about games? Post the questions on the Board.

Record Ideas

 In your Writing Journal, write which of the three games you would most like to play and tell why.

Personal Games Chart

Add a new game you have played to your Personal Games Chart.

Mary Mack

illustrated by Bob Barner

Oh, Mary Mack, Mack, Mack,
All dressed in black, black, black,
With silver buttons, buttons, buttons,
All down her back, back, back.

She asked her mother, mother, mother,
For fifty cents, cents, cents,

To watch the elephant, elephant, elephant,
Jump over the fence, fence, fence.

He jumped so high, high, high,
That he reached the sky, sky, sky,
And he didn't come back, back, back,
'Til the Fourth of July, 'ly, 'ly.

Mary Mack

Meet the Illustrator

Bob Barner studied art in college and became an art teacher. Now he likes to write and illustrate books. "Most of my work [begins] by simple doodles," he says. Now he lives and works in Boston, Massachusetts.

Theme Connections

Talk About It

Rhymes can be used for more activities than hand games. Mary Mack can be used for many different things. Here are some questions to talk about.

- Does this poem tell a story? What is it?
- What other kinds of actions could you do while chanting Mary Mack?
- Would it be more fun to do these activities alone or with someone?
- Do you like playing hand-clapping games? Why or why not?

Check the Concept/Question Board and answer any questions you can. Post any new questions you might have.

Record Ideas

Print the following two questions in your Writing Journal and answer them.

- Do you like playing hand-clapping games? Why or why not?

Say a Verse

Choose a partner. Make up one more verse to "Mary Mack," but use your partner's name. Say the verse to your partner.

FINE Art

Ballplay of the Sioux on the St. Peters River in Winter. 1848. **Seth Eastman.** Oil on canvas. Acquisition in memory of Mitchell A. Wilder, Director, Amon Carter Museum, 1961–1979. Amon Carter Museum, Fort Worth, Texas. 1979.4.

Game Board. Twentieth century. **Dan People**. Liberia. Wood and metal. The Seattle Art Museum, Gift of Katherine White and the Boeing Company.

Matthew and Tilly

Rebecca C. Jones
illustrated by Beth Peck

Matthew and Tilly were friends.

They rode bikes together, and they played hide-and-seek together.

They sold lemonade together.
When business was slow, they
played sidewalk games together.

And sometimes they ate ice-cream
cones together.

Once they even rescued a lady's
kitten from a tree together.

The lady gave them money for the
bubble-gum machines.
  So later they chewed gum together
and remembered how brave they
had been.

Sometimes, though, Matthew and
Tilly got sick of each other.

One day when they were coloring,
Matthew broke Tilly's purple crayon.
He didn't mean to, but he did.
"You broke my crayon," Tilly said in
her crabbiest voice.

"It was an old crayon," Matthew said in his grouchiest voice. "It was ready to break."

"No, it wasn't," Tilly said. "It was a brand-new crayon, and you broke it. You always break everything."

"Stop being so picky," Matthew said.
"You're always so picky and stinky
and mean."

"Well, you're so stupid," Tilly said.
"You're so stupid and stinky and mean."

Matthew stomped up the stairs. By himself.

Tilly found a piece of chalk and
began drawing numbers and squares
on the sidewalk. By herself.

Upstairs, Matthew got out his cash register and some cans so he could play store. He piled the cans extra high, and he put prices on everything.

This was the best store he had ever made. Probably because that picky and stinky and mean old Tilly wasn't around to mess it up.

But he didn't have a customer. And playing store wasn't much fun without a customer.

Tilly finished drawing the numbers and squares. She drew them really big, with lots of squiggly lines. This was the best sidewalk game she had ever drawn.

Probably because that stupid and
stinky and mean old Matthew wasn't
around to mess it up.

But she didn't have anyone to play
with. And a sidewalk game wasn't
much fun without another player.

Matthew looked out the window
and wondered what Tilly was doing.

Tilly looked up at Matthew's window
and wondered what he was doing.

She smiled, just a little. That was
enough for Matthew.
"I'm sorry," he called.
"So am I," said Tilly.

And Matthew ran downstairs so
they could play.
Together again.

Matthew and Tilly

Meet the Author

Rebecca C. Jones used her toys to create adventure stories when she was very young. "I rescued them from kidnappers, pushed them out of the way of speeding trucks, and caught them as they fell from helicopters," she remembers. When she grew older, Rebecca became a reporter to write about real-life stories. She began writing books for kids about real life, like *Matthew and Tilly*, after her own children were born.

Meet the Illustrator

Beth Peck studied drawing at art school and has illustrated many books and stories. Being an illustrator is a dream come true for her. She says it is important to have dreams and to work hard in order to succeed.

Theme Connections

Talk About It

Good friends sometimes quarrel. But they soon get over it. Has this ever happened to you? Here are some questions to talk about.

- Have you ever fought with a friend?
- How did you feel?
- How did you end the fight?
- How did you feel then?

Check the Concept/Question Board and answer any questions you can. Do you have any new questions about games? Post them on the Board.

Record Ideas

- Draw a sad face in your Writing Journal and write about a time you fought with a friend.
- Draw a light bulb and write about how you ended the fight.
- Draw a happy face and write about how it felt when the fight was over.

Tell a Story

Share your story about a fight with a friend with one of your classmates. Pick someone who doesn't know the story already.

Bibliography

Allie's Basketball Dream

by Barbara E. Barber. Is basketball just a boy's game? Allie doesn't think so.

The Great Ball Game: A Muskogee Story

by Joseph Bruchac. Why do birds fly south for the winter? This tale tells all.

Henry and Mudge and the Wild Wind

by Cynthia Rylant. Find out how Dad turns a scary storm into a fun game for Henry and his dog, Mudge.

Max Found Two Sticks

by Brian Pinkney. Max makes music with two twigs.

Finger Rhymes

collected and illustrated by Marc Brown. This is a collection of rhyming finger games including hand-and-finger movements.

Ronald Morgan Goes to Bat

by Patricia Reilly Giff. Ronald can't hit and Ronald can't catch, but his team needs him just the same.

The Tortoise and the Hare

by Janet Stevens. Which of these two do you think would win a race? The answer might surprise you!

What Game Shall We Play?

by Pat Hutchins. What game does Wise Owl say the animal friends should play?

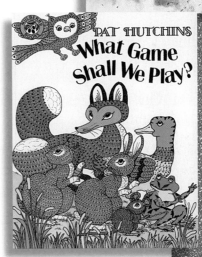

Folktales

Do you have a favorite story? Do you like to tell stories? Stories are fun to hear and fun to tell. They can be silly or they can teach us a lesson. We can go to far away places and meet all kinds of strange and wonderful characters in stories.

MAGIC INK

The Chase

told by Béatrice Tanaka
illustrated by Michel Gay

Coyote was sitting peacefully in the meadow when he saw Rabbit run past, quick as an arrow.

"If Rabbit's running that fast, there must be hunters after him," Coyote said to himself. "I'd better run too."

Moose, who was quietly grazing in the swamp, noticed her two friends running by.

"If Coyote's running that fast, the river must be flooding," Moose said to herself. "I'd better be off too."

Wolf, who had been lazily napping in
his den, was awakened by the galloping
footsteps of the three runners.

"If Moose is running that fast, the
forest must be on fire," said Wolf to
himself. "I'd better put off my nap
until later."

Bear, who was calmly fishing in the stream, saw the four runners racing by at top speed. He recognized his friend Wolf.

"If Wolf is running that fast, the situation must be serious, very serious," thought bear, and he lumbered off after them.

After running a good while, Bear
caught up with Wolf, who was crouched
in a clearing, exhausted and panting.

"What's going on?" demanded Bear. "I
know someone as brave as you wouldn't
run unless there was real danger."

"I have no idea," said Wolf. "It's Moose
we should ask. When I saw her running
so fast, I decided I'd better put off my
nap and follow her."

"Tell us, Moose, why were you
running?"

"I have no idea," said Moose. "It's
Coyote we should ask. When I saw him
run by so fast, I thought I'd better be
off too."

"Say, Coyote, why were you running?"

"I have no idea," said Coyote. "It's Rabbit we should ask. When I saw how fast he was running, I thought I'd better run too. When he stopped, so did I. He'll know what terrible danger we've escaped."

"Hey, Rabbit!" cried Bear, Wolf, Moose, and Coyote together. "Why were we running?"

"Why were *you* running?" said Rabbit.

"I have no idea. But *me*—I was late
for dinner!"

The Chase

Meet the Author

Béatrice Tanaka was born in Romania. She has traveled to many countries including Greece, Morocco, and Japan and can speak many languages. She has always been interested in art and tries to make books that her children can enjoy.

Meet the Illustrator

Michel Gay was born in Lyon, France to a family of musicians. His grandfather encouraged young Michel to become a musician, but Michel was more interested in drawing.

Michel has many friends who describe him as an artistic genius. He has illustrated many stories, including *Rabbit Express*, *The Christmas Wolf*, and *White Owl and Blue Mouse*.

Theme Connections

Think About It

In this folktale, one animal after another gets caught up in the chase. Here are some questions to think about.

- Why did all of the animals chase each other?
- Do you think the animals learned a lesson from the chase?
- Do you think they will each join in a chase again?

Look at the Concept/Question Board. Are there any questions on it that you can answer now? Do you have any new questions about folktales? Write the questions on the Board. Maybe the next reading will help answer your questions.

Record Ideas

 Write your answers to these questions in your Writing Journal.

- Is this a true story?
- How do you know?

Tell a Story

Find a partner and think of some other animals that could join the chase. Add them into the story.

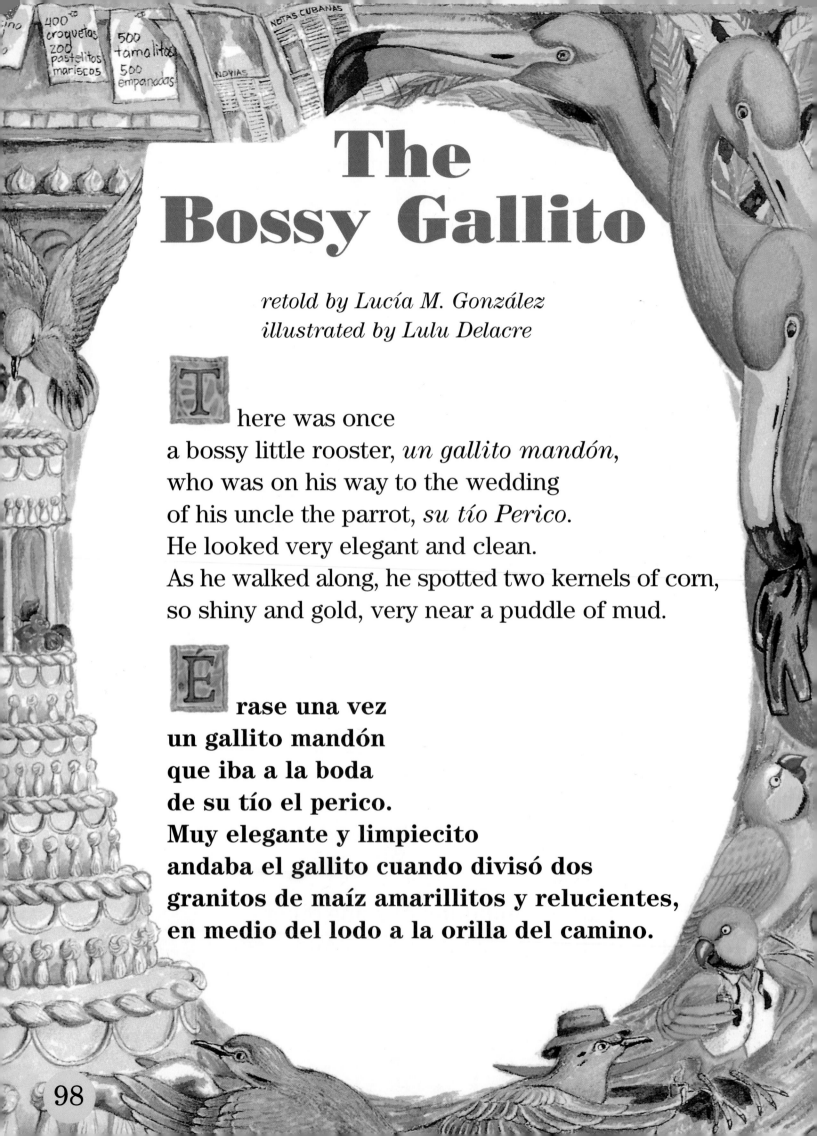

The Bossy Gallito

retold by *Lucía M. González*
illustrated by *Lulu Delacre*

T here was once
a bossy little rooster, *un gallito mandón*,
who was on his way to the wedding
of his uncle the parrot, *su tío Perico*.
He looked very elegant and clean.
As he walked along, he spotted two kernels of corn,
so shiny and gold, very near a puddle of mud.

É rase una vez
un gallito mandón
que iba a la boda
de su tío el perico.
Muy elegante y limpiecito
andaba el gallito cuando divisó dos
granitos de maíz amarillitos y relucientes,
en medio del lodo a la orilla del camino.

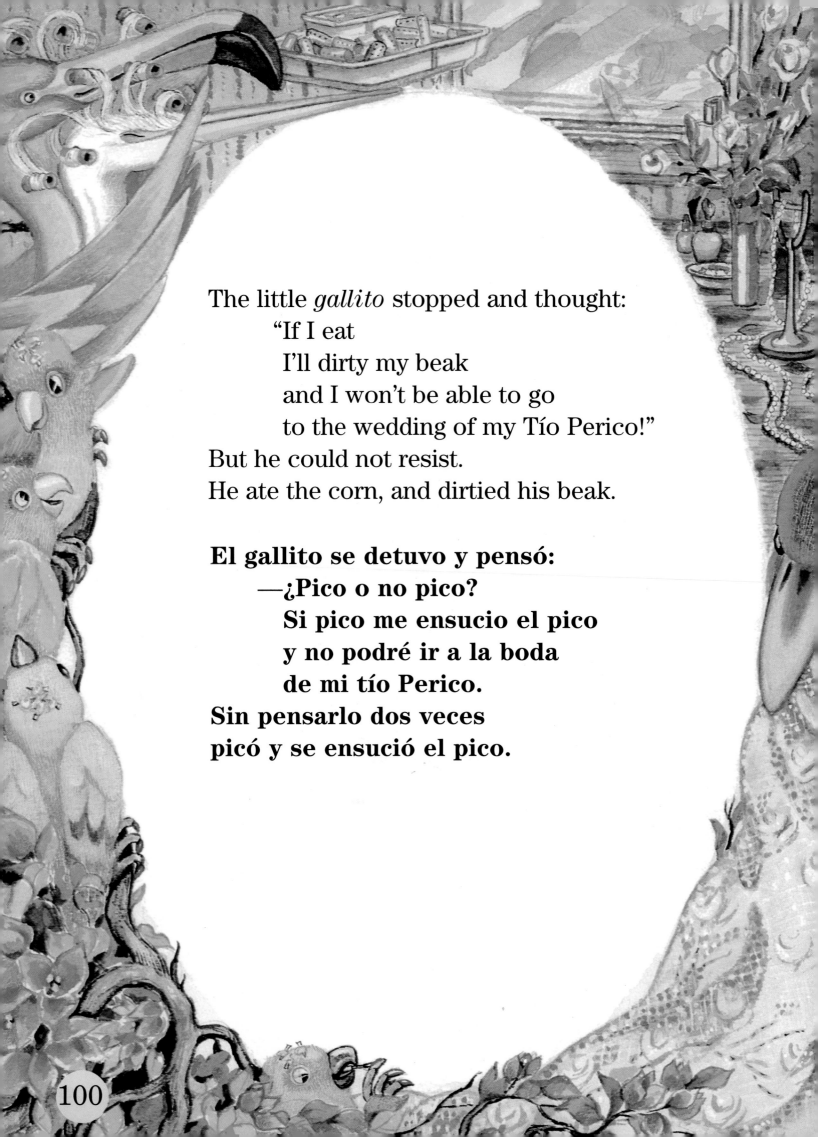

The little *gallito* stopped and thought:
   "If I eat
     I'll dirty my beak
     and I won't be able to go
     to the wedding of my Tío Perico!"
But he could not resist.
He ate the corn, and dirtied his beak.

El gallito se detuvo y pensó:
   —¿Pico o no pico?
     Si pico me ensucio el pico
     y no podré ir a la boda
     de mi tío Perico.
Sin pensarlo dos veces
picó y se ensució el pico.

Just then, he saw some grass to the side
of the road.
So he went to the grass and he said:
    "Grass, clean my *pico*
      so that I can go
      to the wedding of my Tío Perico!"
But the grass said:
    "I will not."

**Más adelante vio la yerba que había al otro lado
del camino.
Entonces le dijo a la yerba:
    —Yerba, límpiame el pico
      para ir a la boda
      de mi tío Perico.
Pero la yerba le contestó:
    —¡No te lo limpiaré!**

101

The little *gallito* walked a little way
until he saw a goat, and he ordered:
  "Goat, eat the grass
    who won't clean my *pico*
    so that I can go
    to the wedding of my Tío Perico!"

But the goat, who didn't like to be
bossed around, said:
"I will not."

**El gallito entonces fue
a donde estaba el chivo y le ordenó:
—Chivo, cómete la yerba
que no me quiere limpiar el pico
para ir a la boda
de mi tío Perico.
Pero el chivo, al que no le gustaba
que lo mandaran, contestó:
—¡No me la comeré!**

The little *gallito* hurried along
until he found a stick, and he scolded:
"Stick, hit the goat
who won't eat the grass
who won't clean my *pico*

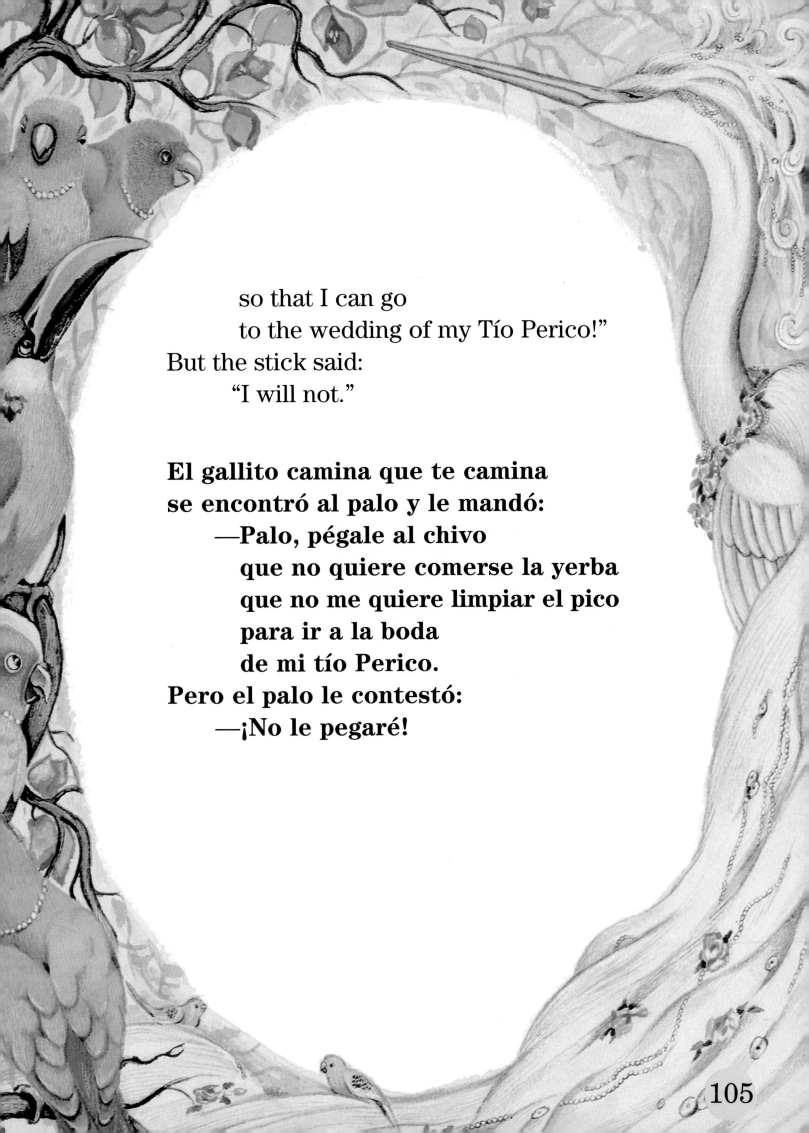

so that I can go
to the wedding of my Tío Perico!"
But the stick said:
"I will not."

El gallito camina que te camina
se encontró al palo y le mandó:
—Palo, pégale al chivo
que no quiere comerse la yerba
que no me quiere limpiar el pico
para ir a la boda
de mi tío Perico.
Pero el palo le contestó:
—¡No le pegaré!

In a nearby bush, the little *gallito* found
a fire burning.
He ran to the bush and demanded of the fire:

"Fire, burn the stick
who won't hit the goat
who won't eat the grass
who won't clean my *pico*
so that I can go
to the wedding of my Tío Perico!"
But the fire said:
"I will not."

El gallito entonces vio al fuego
que ardía entre un matorral cercano y le exigió:
—Fuego, quema el palo
que no quiere pegarle al chivo
que no quiere comerse la yerba
que no me quiere limpiar el pico
para ir a la boda
de mi tío Perico.
Pero el fuego le contestó:
—¡No lo quemaré!

By now, the little *gallito* was in a VERY big hurry.
He rushed to a stream and commanded
the water:

"Water, quench the fire
who won't burn the stick
who won't hit the goat

who won't eat the grass
who won't clean my *pico*
so that I can go
to the wedding of my Tío Perico!"
But the water said:
"I will not."

**Andando muy apresurado, el gallito
se acercó al chorro de agua y le exigió:
—Agua, apaga el fuego
que no quiere quemar el palo
que no quiere pegarle al chivo
que no quiere comerse la yerba
que no me quiere limpiar el pico
para ir a la boda
de mi tío Perico.
Pero el aqua le contestó:
—¡No lo apagaré!**

The little *gallito* did not know what
else to do. Then he saw the sun, *el sol*,
smiling at him from up in the sky. The sun
was his good friend. The little *gallito* always sang
to him first thing in the morning to wake him up.

**El gallito no sabía que más podía hacer. De
repente se fijó en el sol que lo miraba con una
sonrisa desde el cielo. Él era su amigo. El
gallito siempre lo despertaba con su canto
tempranito en la mañana.**

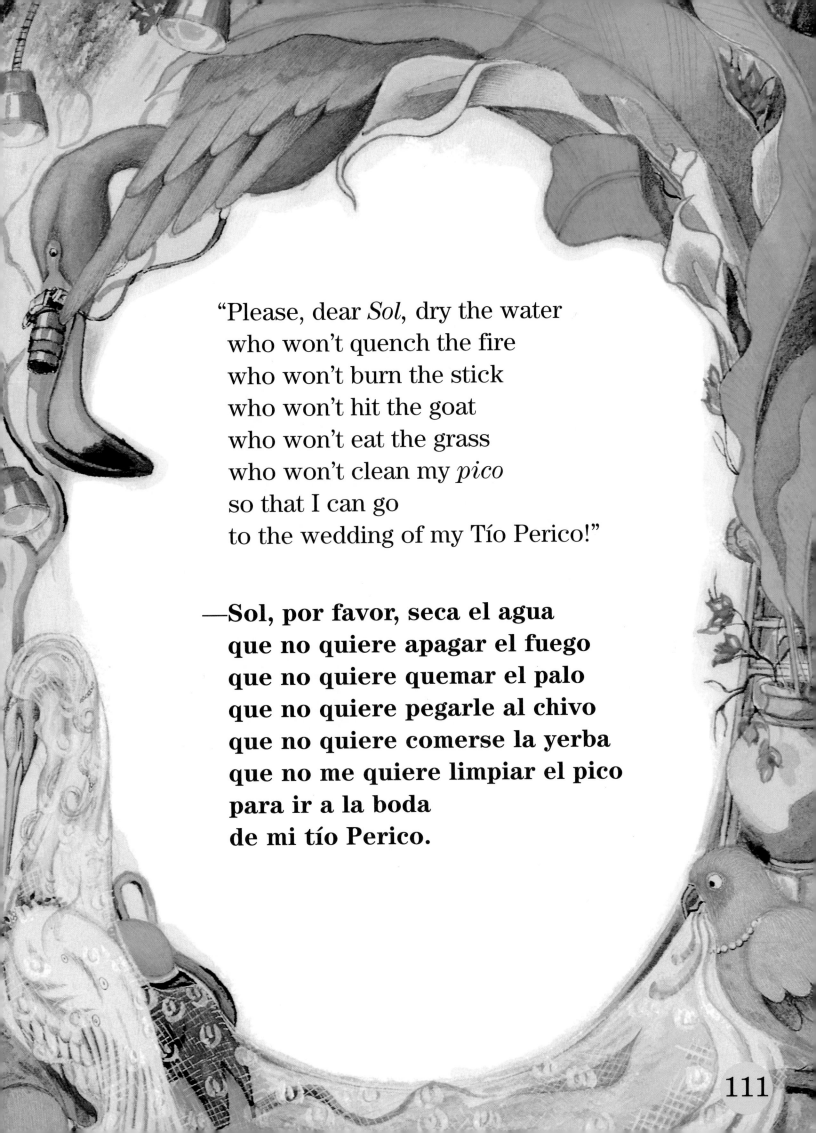

"Please, dear *Sol*, dry the water
who won't quench the fire
who won't burn the stick
who won't hit the goat
who won't eat the grass
who won't clean my *pico*
so that I can go
to the wedding of my Tío Perico!"

—Sol, por favor, seca el agua
que no quiere apagar el fuego
que no quiere quemar el palo
que no quiere pegarle al chivo
que no quiere comerse la yerba
que no me quiere limpiar el pico
para ir a la boda
de mi tío Perico.

And the sun said:
"With pleasure, my friend!
¡Con gran placer!"

Y el sol le contestó:
—¡Con gran placer!

The water, who had heard the sun's
reply, said:

"Pardon me, but I will quench the fire."
And the fire said:

"Pardon me, but I will burn the stick."
And the stick said:

"Pardon me, but I will hit the goat."

Al escuchar al sol, el agua con temor dijo:

—Perdón, yo apagaré el fuego.
Y el fuego dijo:

—Perdón, yo quemaré el palo.
Y el palo dijo:

—Perdón, yo le pegaré al chivo.

And the goat said:

"Pardon me, but I will eat the grass."

And the grass said:

"Pardon me, but I will clean your *pico*."

And so it did.

Y el chivo dijo:

—Perdón, yo me comeré la yerba.

Y la yerba dijo:

—Perdón, yo te limpiaré el pico.

Y así lo hizo.

The little *gallito* thanked his good
friend *el sol* with a long:
"¡QUI-QUI-RI-QUÍ!
COCK-A-DOODLE-DOO!"

**El gallito le dio las gracias a su amigo
el sol con un largo:
—¡QUI-QUI-RI-QUÍ!**

. . . and he rushed the rest of the way to get to the wedding on time.

. . . **y siguió su camino apuradito para llegar a tiempo a la boda de su tío Perico.**

The Bossy Gallito

Meet the Author

Lucía M. González grew up in Cuba listening to storytellers. She moved to the United States at age 12, and later became a storyteller herself. She translates her favorite stories into English to share with children in the United States. As a librarian, author, and storyteller, Gonzalez teaches children about people from many different places by sharing her favorite folktales.

Meet the Illustrator

Lulu Delacre is from Puerto Rico. She says, "When I was ten, my parents enrolled me in drawing lessons and since then, always encouraged me to pursue my artistic abilities." She spends many hours on each drawing and likes to use colored pencils.

Theme Connections

Think About It

Here are some questions to help you think about the story.

- Do you think the rooster learned a lesson?
- Do you think he will ask for help differently next time?

Look at the Concept/Question Board. Are there any questions on it that you can answer now? Do you have any new questions about folktales? Write the questions on the Board. The next reading may help answer your questions.

Record Ideas

 Write your answers to these questions in your Writing Journal.

- Did you like this story?
- Why or why not?

Draw a Picture

Divide a piece of paper in half. On one side, draw how the rooster feels when he doesn't get help. On the other side, draw how the rooster would feel if he got help.

Anansi and the Talking Melon

retold by Eric A. Kimmel
illustrated by Janet Stevens

One fine morning Anansi the Spider sat high up in a thorn tree looking down into Elephant's garden. Elephant was hoeing his melon patch. The ripe melons seemed to call out to Anansi, "Look how juicy and sweet we are! Come eat us!"

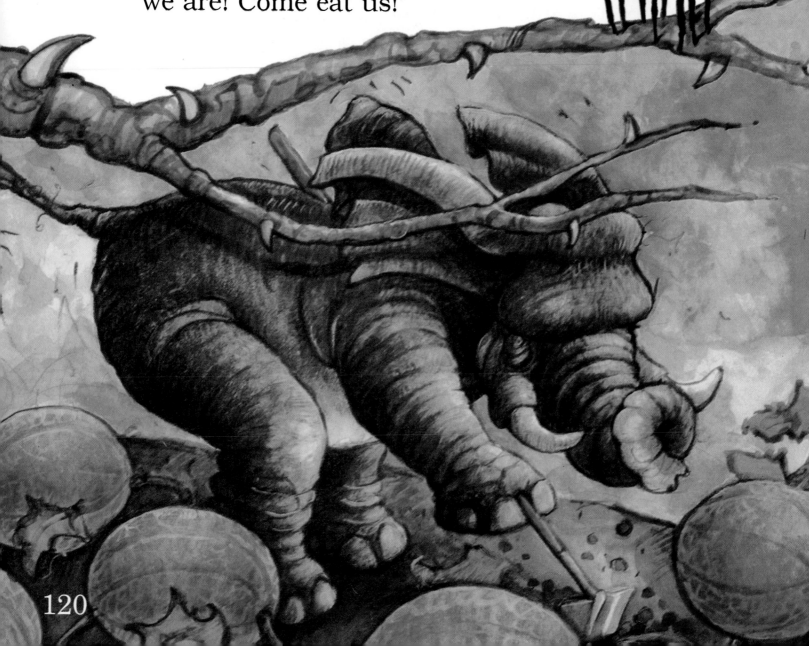

Anansi loved to eat melons, but
he was much too lazy to grow them
himself. So he sat up in the thorn
tree, watching and waiting, while
the sun rose high in the sky and
the day grew warm.

By the time noon came, it was too hot to work. Elephant put down his hoe and went inside his house to take a nap.

Here was the moment Anansi had been waiting for. He broke off a thorn and dropped down into the melon patch. He used the thorn to bore a hole in the biggest, ripest melon.

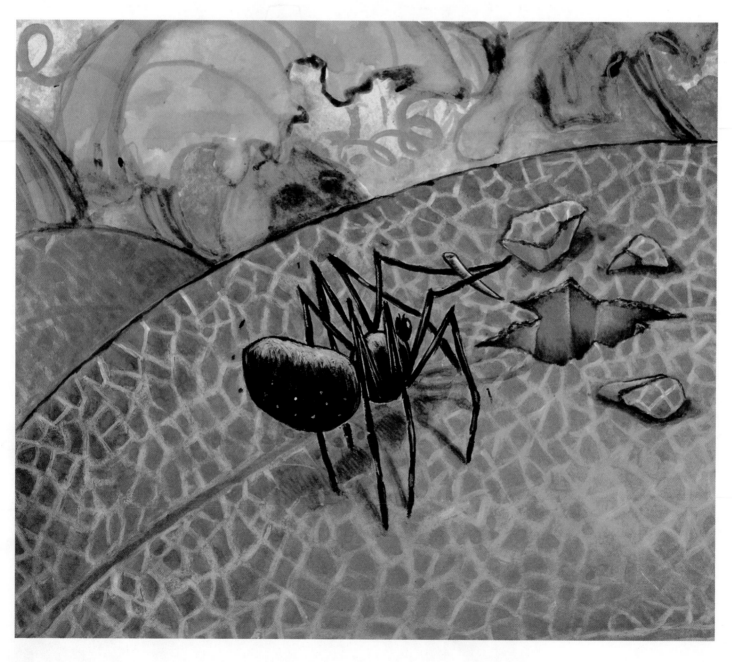

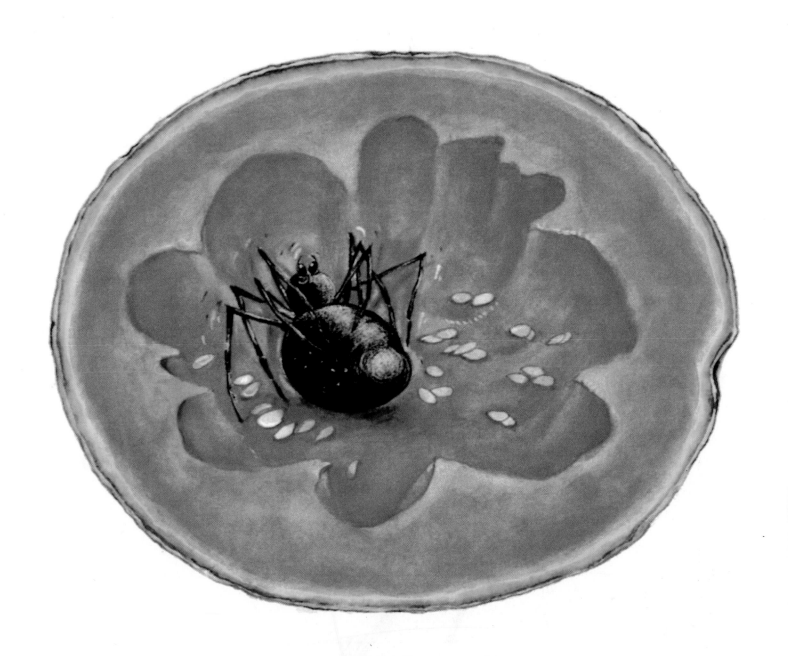

Anansi squeezed inside and started eating. He ate and ate until he was as round as a berry.

"I'm full," Anansi said at last. "Elephant will be coming back soon. It is time to go."

But when he tried to squeeze through the hole, Anansi had a surprise. He didn't fit! The hole was big enough for a thin spider, but much too small for a fat one.

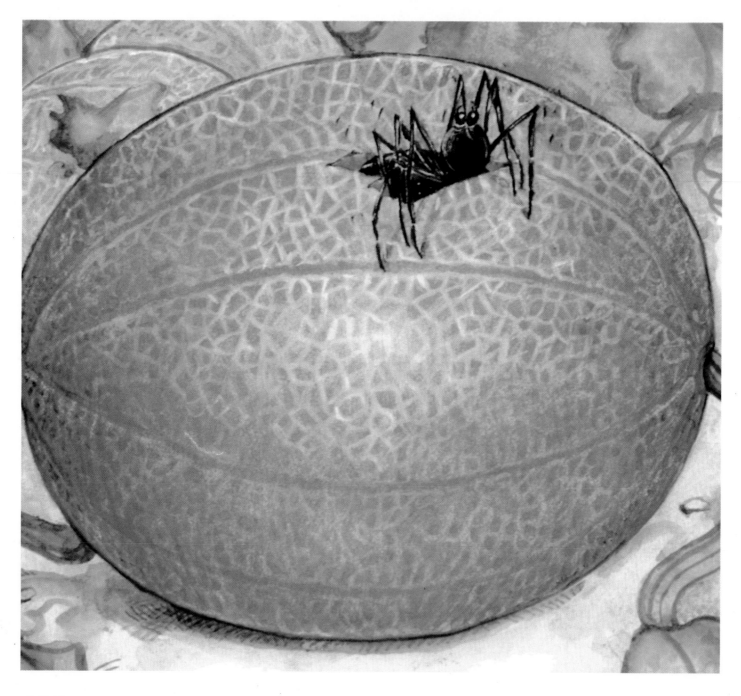

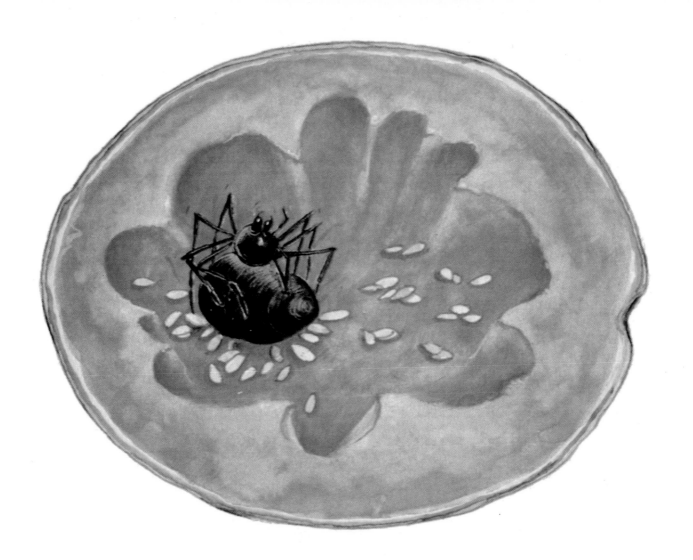

"I'm stuck!" Anansi cried. "I can't get out. I will have to wait until I am thin again."

Anansi sat down on a pile of melon seeds and waited to get thin. Time passed slowly.

"I'm bored," Anansi said. "I wish I had something to do."

Just then he heard Elephant
returning to the garden. Anansi
had an idea. "When Elephant
gets closer, I will say something.
Elephant will think the melon is
talking. What fun!"

Elephant walked over to the
melon patch. "Look at this fine melon.
How big and ripe it is!" he said,
picking it up.

"Ouch!" cried Anansi.

Elephant jumped. "Aah! Who said that?"

"I did. The melon," Anansi said.

"I didn't know melons could talk," said Elephant.

"Of course we do. We talk all the time. The trouble is, you never listen."

"I can't believe my ears!" Elephant exclaimed. "A talking melon! Who could believe it? I must show this to the king."

Elephant ran down the road, carrying the melon with Anansi inside. Along the way, he ran into Hippo.

"Where are you going with that melon?" Hippo asked.

"I'm taking it to the king," Elephant told him.

"What for? The king has hundreds of melons."

"He doesn't have one like this," Elephant said. "This is a talking melon."

Hippo didn't believe Elephant. "A talking melon? What an idea! That's as ridiculous as . . ."

". . . a skinny hippo," the melon said.

Hippo got so angry his face turned red.

"Who said that? Did you say that, Elephant?"

"It wasn't me. It was the melon," Elephant said. "I told you it talks. Do you believe me now?"

"I do!" Hippo exclaimed. "I want to go with you. I want to hear what the king says when you show him this talking melon."

"Come along, then," said Elephant.

So Elephant and Hippo went down the road together, carrying the melon.

By and by, they ran into Warthog. "Where are you taking that melon?" Warthog asked them.

"We're taking it to the king," Elephant and Hippo told him.

131

"What for? The king has hundreds of melons," Warthog said.

"He doesn't have one like this," Hippo replied. "This melon talks. I heard it."

Warthog started to laugh. "A talking melon? Why, that's as ridiculous as . . ."

". . . a handsome warthog," said the melon.

Warthog got so angry he shook all over. "Who said that? Did you say that, Elephant? Did you say that, Hippo?"

"Of course not!" Hippo and Elephant told him. "The melon talks. Do you believe us now?"

"I do!" cried Warthog. "Let me go with you. I want to see what the king does when you show him this talking melon."

So Warthog, Elephant, and Hippo went down the road together, carrying the melon.

Along the way, they met Ostrich, Rhino, and Turtle.

They didn't believe the melon could talk either until they heard it for themselves. Then they wanted to come along too.

The animals came before the king.
Elephant bowed low as he placed
the melon at the king's feet.

The king looked down. "Why did
you bring me a melon?" he asked
Elephant. "I have hundreds of
melons growing in my garden."

"You don't have one like this," Elephant said. "This melon talks."

"A talking melon? I don't believe it. Say something, Melon." The king prodded the melon with his foot.

The melon said nothing.

137

"Melon," the king said in a slightly louder voice, "there is no reason to be shy. Say whatever you like. I only want to hear you talk."

The melon still said nothing. The king grew impatient.

"Melon, if you can talk, I want you to say something. I command you to speak."

The melon did not make a sound.

The king gave up. "Oh, this is a stupid melon!" he said.

Just then the melon spoke. "Stupid, am I? Why do you say that? I'm not the one who talks to melons!"

The animals had never seen the king so angry. "How dare this melon insult me!" he shouted. The king picked up the melon and hurled it as far as he could.

The melon bounced and rolled all the way to Elephant's house. KPOM! It smacked into the thorn tree and burst into pieces. Anansi picked himself up from among the bits of melon rind.

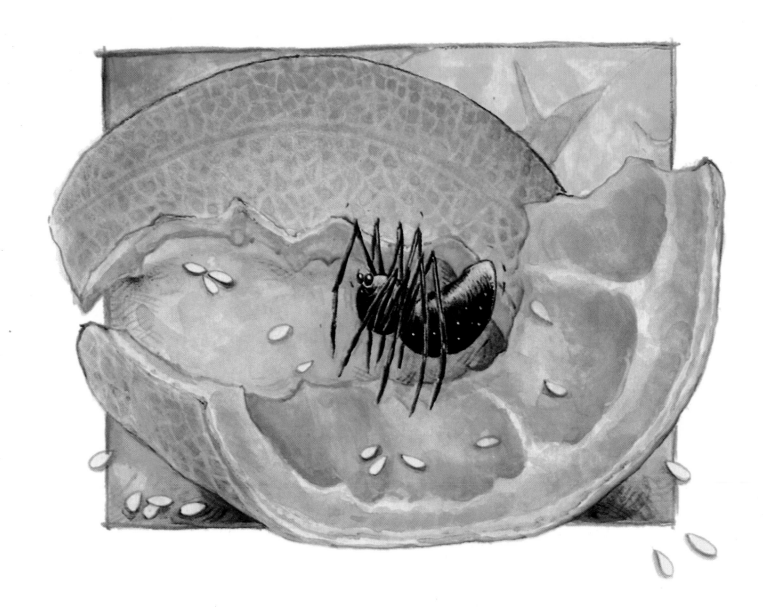

All the excitement had made him
thin. And now that he was thin
again, he was hungry. Anansi
climbed the banana tree. He settled
himself in the middle of a big bunch
of bananas and started eating.

Elephant returned. He went
straight to the melon patch.

"You melons got me in trouble with the king!" Elephant said. "From now on, you can talk all you like. I'm not going to listen to a word you say!"

"Good for you, Elephant!" Anansi called from the bananas. "We bananas should have warned you. Talking melons are nothing but trouble."

Anansi and the Talking Melon

Meet the Author

Eric A. Kimmel said, "I was born to be a writer. I never wanted to be anything else." Eric A. Kimmel's favorite book as a child was *Horton Hatches the Egg* by Dr. Seuss. He wanted to write a book like that and have his name on the cover. When Eric was older, he finally did. In fact, he has written a lot of books.

Meet the Illustrator

Janet Stevens grew up in many places, such as Italy and Hawaii. She has always been interested in art. She loves animals and likes to draw them in her books.

Theme Connections

Think About It

Animals in folktales often talk and act the same way people do. Here are some questions to think about.

- Why did the animals believe the melon could talk?
- Did the animals learn a lesson?
- What was it?
- Will they think a melon can talk if this happens again?

Look at the Concept/Question Board. Can you answer any questions now? Do you have any new questions about folktales? Write the questions on the Board. Maybe the next reading will help answer your questions.

Record Ideas

Write your answers to these questions in your Writing Journal.

- Is this a true story?
- How do you know?

Create A Cartoon

Pretend you met Elephant carrying the melon with Anansi inside it. What might Anansi say to you? Draw a cartoon and write the words in a speech bubble.

FINE Art

Coyote Koshare. 1993. **Harry Fonseca.** Mixed media on canvas. 24 × 30 in. Courtesy of Harry Fonseca.

Battle scene from the comic opera "The Seafarer." 1923. **Paul Klee.** Watercolor. Trix Durst-Haase Collection, Basel, Switzerland. ©1999 Paul Klee Foundation/Artists Rights Society (ARS), New York. Photo: Eric Lessing/Art Resource, NY.

Bunraku performance in Osaka, Japan. Photo: Werner
Forman Archive/Art Resource, NY.

Peter and the Wolf. 1943. **Ben Shahn.** Tempera. $6\frac{1}{2} \times 10$ in.
Private collection. ©1999 Estate of Ben Shahn/Licensed by
VAGA, New York, NY. Photo: Scala/Art Resource, NY.

The Three Billy Goats Gruff

a folktale retold by Christine Crocker

illustrated by Holly Hannon

Once upon a time there were three billy goat brothers named Gruff. The three billy goats lived by a river. Across the river was a meadow with tall green grass.

One day, the billy goats wanted to cross the river to eat the grass. But there was only one bridge across the river. And under that bridge lived a mean, hungry troll. The troll had eyes as big as saucers and a nose as long as a poker.

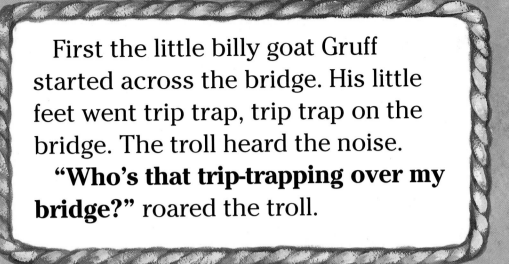

First the little billy goat Gruff started across the bridge. His little feet went trip trap, trip trap on the bridge. The troll heard the noise.

"Who's that trip-trapping over my bridge?" roared the troll.

"It is only I, the little billy goat Gruff," said the goat in his tiny voice. **"I'll eat you for my breakfast!"** said the troll.

"Oh, please don't," said the goat. "I'm much too small. Wait until my big brother comes. He'd be a much better breakfast for a big troll like you."

"Very well," said the greedy troll. So he let the little billy goat Gruff cross the bridge.

Next, the middle-sized billy goat Gruff started across the bridge. His middle-sized feet went trip trap, trip trap.

"Who's that trip-trapping over my bridge?" shouted the troll.

"It's only I, the middle-sized billy goat Gruff," said the goat in his middle-sized voice.

"I'll eat you for my breakfast!" roared the troll. And he jumped up on the bridge.

"Oh, please don't," said the goat. "I'm much too small. Wait for my big brother. He'd be a much better meal for a big troll like you."

"Very well," said the greedy troll. So he let the middle-sized billy goat Gruff cross the bridge.

Soon the big billy goat Gruff started across the bridge. His big feet went trip trap, trip trap. The bridge shook.

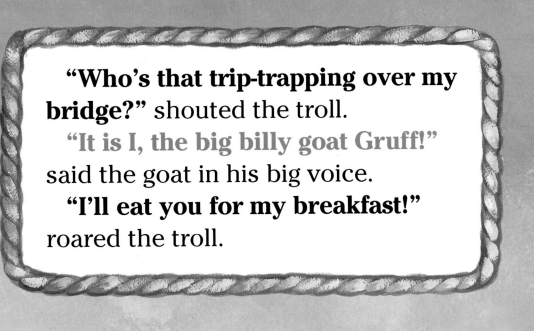

"**Who's that trip-trapping over my bridge?**" shouted the troll.

"It is I, the big billy goat Gruff!" said the goat in his big voice.

"**I'll eat you for my breakfast!**" roared the troll.

"Oh no, you won't," said the goat. The big billy goat Gruff ran at the troll and butted him into the river. The troll was never heard of again.

Then the three billy goats Gruff went into the meadow. They ate all the grass they wanted and lived happily ever after. And so—
Snip, snap, snout,
This tale's told out.

The Three Billy Goats Gruff

Meet the Illustrator

Holly Hannon has worked as a professional illustrator for thirteen years. Her works come from the joy found in brilliant colors and beautiful surroundings. She lives with her husband in Seneca, South Carolina where she enjoys gardening, hiking, cooking, and reading about all three.

Theme Connections

Talk About It

Here are some questions to think about. Then join a small group and talk about them.

- Is this a true story?
- How do you know?

Look at the Concept/Question Board. Are there any questions on it that you can answer now? Do you have any new questions about folktales? Write the questions on the Board. Maybe the next reading will help answer your questions.

Record Ideas

 Write your answers to these two questions in your Writing Journal.

- Did you like this story? Why or why not?

Use Story Character Voices

Divide into groups of four. Each group member can choose one of the story characters to act out. Tell the story together. Remember to speak in the voice of your story character.

Little Green Riding Hood

retold by Gianni Rodari

illustrated by Nadine Bernard Westcott

Grandpa: Once upon a time there was a little girl called Little Yellow Riding Hood.

Child: No! Red Riding Hood!

Grandpa: Oh yes, of course, Red Riding Hood.
Well, one day her mother called and said:
"Little Green Riding Hood—"

Child: Red!

Grandpa: Sorry! Red.
"Now, my child, go to Aunt Mary and take her these potatoes."

Child: No! It doesn't go like that!
"Go to Grandma and take her these cakes."

Grandpa: All right.
So the little girl went off, and in the
wood she met a giraffe.

Child: What a mess you're making of it!
It was a wolf!

Grandpa: And the wolf said:
"What's six times eight?"

Child: No! No! The wolf asked her where
she was going.

Grandpa: So he did. And Little Black Riding Hood
replied—

Child: Red! Red!! Red!!!

Grandpa: She replied: "I'm going to the market to buy some tomatoes."

Child: No she didn't. She said: "I'm going to my Grandma, who is sick, but I've lost my way."

Grandpa: Of course! And the horse said—

Child: What horse? It was a wolf.

Grandpa: So it was. And this is what it said: "Take the 75 bus, get out at the main square, turn right, and at the first doorway you'll find three steps. Leave the steps where they are, but pick up the dime you'll find lying on them, and buy yourself a packet of chewing gum."

Child: Grandpa, you're terribly bad at telling stories. You get them all wrong, but all the same, I wouldn't mind some chewing gum.

Grandpa: All right here's your dime. Now I'll finish reading my newspaper.

Little Green Riding Hood

Meet the Author

Gianni Rodari was an Italian author. He wrote stories and poems. He also wrote for magazines and newspapers. He believed that fairy tales could help people think about the world. He once said: "There is nothing more beautiful in the world than a child's smile."

Meet the Illustrator

Nadine Bernard Westcott grew up in New Jersey and spent her summers in Vermont. Her first memory of drawing was doing sketches on paper napkins in restaurants. Later, she studied art in college and started drawing greeting cards as well as books.

Theme Connections

Talk About It

Think about the differences between Little Red Riding Hood and this story as you talk about these questions.

- How did the grandpa change the story?
- Why did he change the story?
- Do you think the grandpa really did not know the story?
- Do you think that it is okay to change a story like the grandpa did?

Look at the Concept/Question Board. Can you answer any questions now? Do you have any new questions about folktales? Write the questions on the Board. Maybe the next reading will help answer your question.

Record Ideas

 Compare Little Red Riding Hood and Little Green Riding Hood in your Writing Journal.

Tell a Story

Choose a partner. Pick one of your favorite fairy tales and make up a silly version. Have your partner guess the name of the real fairy tale. Then have your partner take a turn.

Bibliography

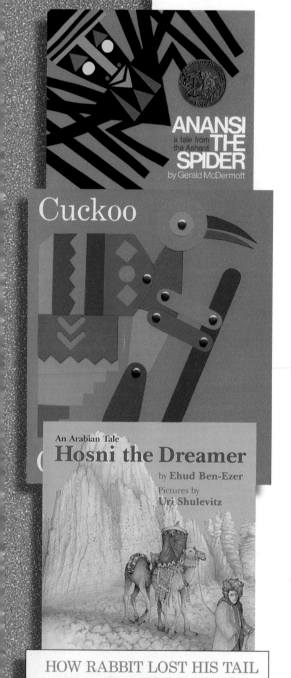

Anansi the Spider: a tale from the Ashanti

by Gerald McDermott. Something you see at night is the reward Anansi gave his sons. What is it?

Cuckoo: A Mexican Folktale

by Lois Ehlert. What can you tell about a bird by looking at its feathers?

Hosni the Dreamer: An Arabian Tale

by Ehud Ben-Ezer. Could buying a verse save your life and bring you happiness? Find out what happens to Hosni.

How Rabbit Lost His Tail

by Ann Tompert. Why is Rabbit up a willow tree? What does he leave there?

It Could Always Be Worse

by Margot Zemach. What happens to peace in the family when all the barnyard animals move into the house?

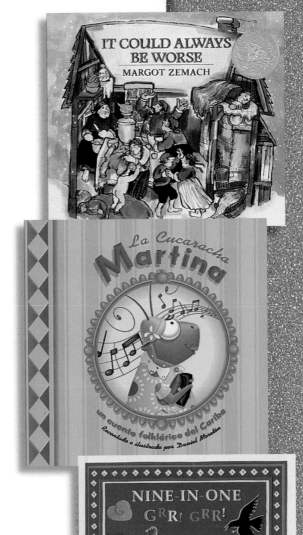

La Cucaracha Martina: A Caribbean Folktale

by Daniel Moreton. What music is the sweetest? Ask the cockroach. She knows.

Nine-in-One, Grr! Grr!

by Blia Xiong, adapted by Cathy Spagnoli. How does Bird stop Tiger from giving Shao nine tiger cubs every year?

Tops and Bottoms

by Janet Stevens. Find out what Hare is up to while Bear snoozes in his favorite chair.

Glossary

Pronunciation Key

a as in **a**t	**ī** as in k**i**te	**o͞o** as in t**oo**	**ə** as in **a**bout, chick**e**n, penc**i**l, cann**o**n, circ**u**s	**sh** as in **sh**op
ā as in l**a**te	**o** as in **o**x	**or** as in f**or**m		**th** as in **th**in
â as in c**a**re	**ō** as in r**o**se	**ou** as in **ou**t	**ch** as in **ch**air	**t͟h** as in **th**ere
ä as in f**a**ther	**ô** as in b**ou**ght and r**aw**	**u** as in **u**p	**hw** as in **wh**ich	**zh** as in trea**s**ure
e as in s**e**t		**yo͞o** as in **u**se	**ng** as in ri**ng**	
ē as in m**e**	**oi** as in c**oi**n	**ûr** as in t**ur**n; g**er**m, l**ear**n, f**ir**m, w**or**k		
i as in **i**t	**o͝o** as in b**oo**k			

The mark (´) is placed after a syllable with a heavy accent, as in **chicken** (chik´ ən).

The mark (´) after a syllable shows a lighter accent, as in **disappear** (dis´ ə pēr´).

B

bore (bor) *v.* To make a hole.

C

command (kə mand´) *v.* To tell someone to do something in a forceful way.

coyote (kī ō´ tē) *n.* A gray animal that looks like a small wolf.

crabby (krab´ ē) *adj.* Grumpy.

cross (krôs) *v.* Angry.

crouch (krouch) *v.* To get down close to the ground without lying down.

crouch

H

hoe (hō) *v.* To dig with a tool.

D

demand (di mand´) *v.* To ask for something in a bossy way.

doorway (dor´ wā) *n.* Entrance to a room.

I

impatient (im pā´ shənt) *adj.* Not willing to wait.

L

lumber (lum´ bər) *v.* To walk in a heavy way.

E

elegant (e´ li gənt) *adj.* Very dressy and high class.

exhausted (ig zôs´ təd) *adj.* Very tired.

M

meadow (me´ dō) *n.* An open field covered with grass and wildflowers.

meadow

G

gallop (ga´ ləp) *v.* To run quickly.

greedy (grē´ dē) *adj.* Always wanting more.

grouchy (grou´ chē) *adj.* In a bad mood.

grumble (grum´ bəl) *v.* To rumble.

N

nuzzle (nuz´ əl) *v.* To rub with the nose.

O

order (or´ dər) *v.* To say something in a forceful way.

P

packet (pak´ ət) *n.* A small package.

patch (pach) *n.* A small piece of ground on which one kind of plant grows.

patch

picky (pik´ ē) *adj.* Hard to please.

pleasure (ple´ zhər) *n.* Something that makes one happy.

poker (pōk´ ûr) *n.* A metal rod for stirring fires.

poker

prod (prod) *v.* Poke.

purr (pûr) *v.* A sound a cat makes when it is happy.

Q

quench (kwench) *v.* To put out.

R

rescue (res´ ko͞o) *v.* To save from danger.

177

Pronunciation Key: at; lāte; câre; fäther; set; mē; it; kīte; ox; rōse; ô in bought; coin; bŏŏk; tōō; form; out; up; ūse; tûrn; ə sound in about, chicken, pencil, cannon, circus; chair; hw in which; ring; shop; thin; ŧHere; zh in treasure.

resist (ri zist´) *v.* To stay away from.

ridiculous (ri dik´ ū ləs) *adj.* Foolish.

S

saucer (sä sûr) *n.* A small shallow dish for holding a cup.

saucer

scold (skōld) *v.* To say something in a mean way, as if to punish.

serious (sir´ ē əs) *adj.* Not to be taken lightly; important.

situation (si´ chə wā´ shən) *n.* An event; something that is happening.

stomp (stomp) *v.* To stamp with the foot.

T

thorn tree (thorn trē) *n.* A tree with short pointed growth.

thorn tree

trip (trip) *v.* To hit a foot against something so as to fall.

W

wiggle (wig´əl) *v.* To squirm or twist.